Outward-Focused in Color

A PRAYER COLORING JOURNAL

BY DAVE E. COLE

DESIGNED BY JON WREN

Outward-Focused Network
Outward-Focused in Color: A Prayer Coloring Journal
by Dave E. Cole
designed by Jon Wren

Outward-Focused Network
P.O. Box 1062
Duvall, WA 98019

Published in the United States by Outward-Focused Network LLC. Designed, Illustrated and Edited by Jon and Sara Wren, Wren Designed LLP, Snoqualmie, WA.

ISBN-13: 978-1-946210-10-4

Printed by Thomas Shore Publishing, LLC

PRAYING IN COLOR

Our hope at Outward Focused Network, is to come alongside you and empower you to be on mission. No matter who you are, it is vital to spend time with God and explore that relationship creatively. Creativity plays a major role in the missional process. Coming out of the work Dave Cole did with *Re-Focus*, the idea presented itself to create a coloring book that illustrated some of the ideas from our missional conversations.

At face value, this is indeed a coloring book; however, it can be much, much more. As you color and flip through the pages, may you encounter God with every stroke. When you encounter scriptures or thoughts throughout the book, we encourage you to enter into them with an open heart and a creative mind. As you are creative with color, ask the Holy Spirit to give you creative outward-focused ideas. This book is designed to become your prayer journal, using the ACTS plus I model. Adoration, Confession, Thanksgiving, Supplication, and Intercession are the building blocks to a powerful prayer journal.

There is nothing special about these designs; but, if you are willing, the Lord can do some powerful work as you *pray in color*.

WHO IS OFN?

Outward Focused Network (OFN) was created by Dr. Dave E. Cole with hopes of providing a solution for an ongoing issue he saw plaguing churches across the nation. Over time, all organizations experience mission fog, losing sight of why they started or what their mission is.

OFN seeks to create conversations, opportunities, and avenues to combat inward-focused culture that allows mission drift and push towards an outward-focused culture that takes serious the mission God has given all of us.

Want to learn more? Visit us online at:

OUTWARDFOCUSEDNETWORK.COM

Adoration

"THEREFORE, GOD ELEVATED HIM TO THE PLACE OF HIGHEST HONOR
AND GAVE HIM THE NAME ABOVE ALL OTHER NAMES."

- PHILIPPIANS 2:9 (NLT)

_____

_____

_____

_____

_____

_____

_____

_____

_____

_____

_____

Confession

"CREATE IN ME A CLEAN HEART, O GOD.
RENEW A LOYAL SPIRIT WITHIN ME."

- PSALM 51:10 (NLT)

_____
_____
_____
_____
_____
_____
_____
_____
_____
_____
_____
_____
_____
_____

"LET US MAKE MANKIND IN OUR IMAGE, IN OUR LIKENESS, SO THAT THEY MAY RULE OVER THE FISH IN THE SEA AND THE BIRDS IN THE SKY, OVER THE LIVESTOCK AND ALL THE WILD ANIMALS, AND OVER ALL THE CREATURES THAT MOVE ALONG THE GROUND. SO GOD CREATED MANKIND IN HIS OWN IMAGE, IN THE IMAGE OF GOD HE CREATED THEM; MALE AND FEMALE HE CREATED THEM. GOD BLESSED THEM AND SAID TO THEM, 'BE FRUITFUL AND INCREASE IN NUMBERS, FILL THE EARTH AND SUBDUE IT. RULE OVER THE FISH IN THE SEA AND THE BIRDS IN THE SKY AND OVER EVERY LIVING CREATURE THAT MOVES ON THE GROUND.'"

- Genesis 1:26

THANKSGIVING

"BE THANKFUL IN ALL CIRCUMSTANCES, FOR THIS IS GOD'S WILL FOR YOU WHO BELONG TO CHRIST JESUS."

— 1 THESSALONIANS 5:18 (NLT)

_____

_____

_____

_____

_____

_____

_____

_____

_____

_____

_____

_____

_____

Supplication

"GIVE ALL YOUR WORRIES AND CARES TO GOD,
FOR HE CARES ABOUT YOU."

- 1 PETER 5:7 (NLT)

_____
_____
_____
_____
_____
_____
_____
_____
_____
_____
_____
_____

THE
OUTWARD-FOCUSED
GOD IS LIKE
THE CONDUCTOR
OF THE ORCHESTRA

INTERCESSION

"I URGE YOU, FIRST OF ALL, TO PRAY FOR ALL PEOPLE. ASK GOD TO HELP THEM; INTERCEDE ON THEIR BEHALF, AND GIVE THANKS FOR THEM. PRAY THIS WAY FOR KINGS AND ALL WHO ARE IN AUTHORITY SO THAT WE CAN LIVE PEACEFUL AND QUIET LIVES MARKED BY GODLINESS AND DIGNITY. THIS IS GOOD AND PLEASES GOD OUR SAVIOR, WHO WANTS EVERYONE TO BE SAVED AND TO UNDERSTAND THE TRUTH. FOR, THERE IS ONE GOD AND ONE MEDIATOR WHO CAN RECONCILE GOD AND HUMANITY—THE MAN CHRIST JESUS."

- 1 TIMOTHY 2:1-5 (NLT)

PRAYER FOR FAMILY:
_____

_____

PRAYER FOR NEIGHBORS:
_____

_____

PRAYER FOR COMMUNITY:
_____

_____

PRAYER FOR COUNTRY:
_____

_____

PRAYER FOR WORLD:
_____

_____

Adoration

"YOURS, O LORD, IS THE GREATNESS, THE POWER, THE GLORY, THE VICTORY, AND THE MAJESTY. EVERYTHING IN THE HEAVENS AND ON EARTH IS YOURS, O LORD, AND THIS IS YOUR KINGDOM. WE ADORE YOU AS THE ONE WHO IS OVER ALL THINGS. WEALTH AND HONOR COME FROM YOU ALONE, FOR YOU RULE OVER EVERYTHING. POWER AND MIGHT ARE IN YOUR HAND, AND AT YOUR DISCRETION PEOPLE ARE MADE GREAT AND GIVEN STRENGTH."

- 1 CHRONICLES 29:11-12 (NLT)

_____

_____

_____

_____

_____

_____

_____

_____

_____

_____

_____

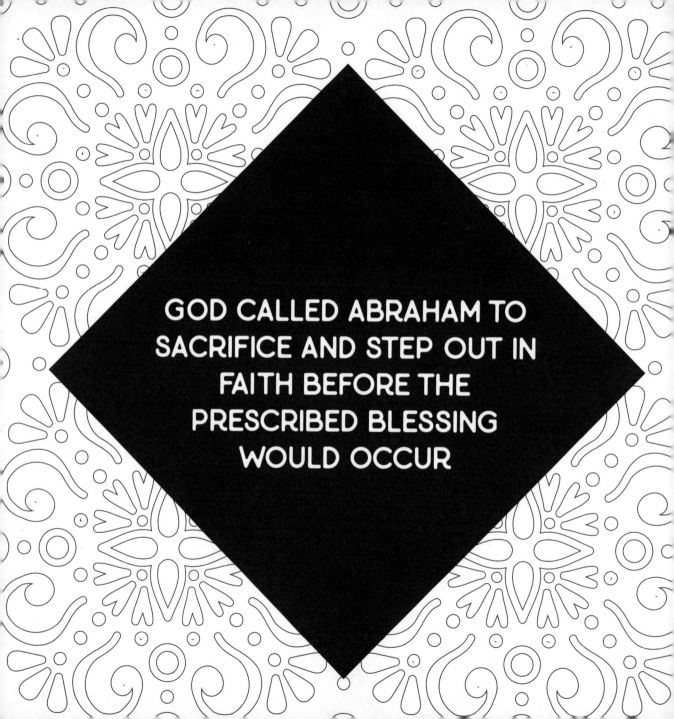

GOD CALLED ABRAHAM TO SACRIFICE AND STEP OUT IN FAITH BEFORE THE PRESCRIBED BLESSING WOULD OCCUR

Confession

"BUT IF WE CONFESS OUR SINS TO HIM, HE IS FAITHFUL AND JUST TO FORGIVE US OUR SINS AND TO CLEANSE US FROM ALL WICKEDNESS."

- 1 JOHN 1:9 (NLT)

THANKSGIVING

"THE TRUMPETERS AND SINGERS PERFORMED TOGETHER IN UNISON TO PRAISE AND GIVE THANKS TO THE LORD. ACCOMPANIED BY TRUMPETS, CYMBALS, AND OTHER INSTRUMENTS, THEY RAISED THEIR VOICES AND PRAISED THE LORD WITH THESE WORDS: 'HE IS GOOD! HIS FAITHFUL LOVE ENDURES FOREVER!' AT THAT MOMENT A THICK CLOUD FILLED THE TEMPLE OF THE LORD."

- 2 CHRONICLES 5:13 (NLT)

_____

_____

_____

_____

_____

_____

_____

_____

_____

_____

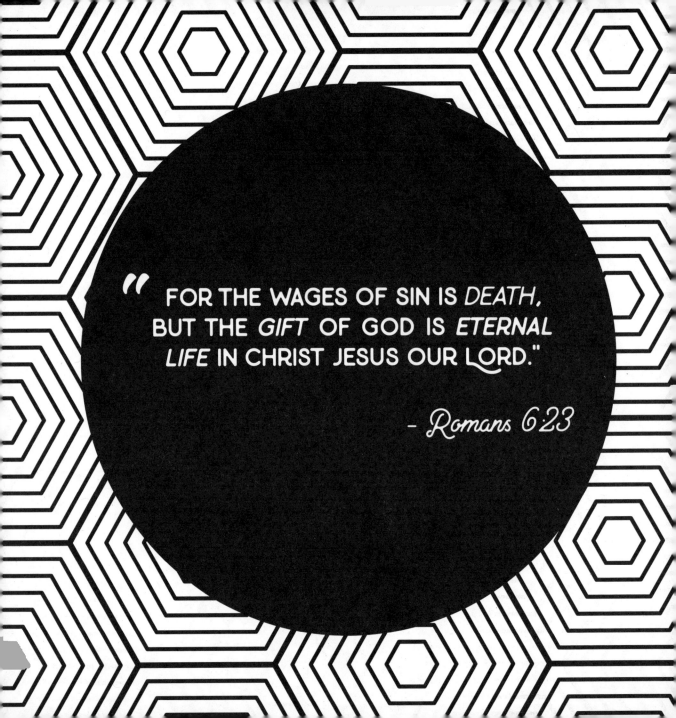

"FOR THE WAGES OF SIN IS *DEATH*, BUT THE *GIFT* OF GOD IS *ETERNAL LIFE* IN CHRIST JESUS OUR LORD."

- Romans 6:23

Supplication

"AND THE HOLY SPIRIT HELPS US IN OUR WEAKNESS. FOR EXAMPLE, WE DON'T KNOW WHAT GOD WANTS US TO PRAY FOR. BUT THE HOLY SPIRIT PRAYS FOR US WITH GROANINGS THAT CANNOT BE EXPRESSED IN WORDS."

- ROMANS 8:26 (NLT)

_____

_____

_____

_____

_____

_____

_____

_____

_____

_____

_____

_____

_____

INTERCESSION

"PRAY IN THE SPIRIT AT ALL TIMES AND ON EVERY OCCASION.
STAY ALERT AND BE PERSISTENT IN YOUR PRAYERS FOR ALL
BELIEVERS EVERYWHERE."

- EPHESIANS 6:18 (NLT)

PRAYER FOR FAMILY:
_____
_____

PRAYER FOR NEIGHBORS:
_____
_____

PRAYER FOR COMMUNITY:
_____
_____

PRAYER FOR COUNTRY:
_____
_____

PRAYER FOR WORLD:
_____
_____

WHO IS YOUR NEIGHBOR?
LIST YOUR NEIGHBORS NAMES, KIDS, JOBS, ETC. AND PRAY FOR THEM.

MY HOME

DRAW A MAP OF YOUR TOWN

WHO HAS GOD STRATEGICALLY PLACED YOU NEAR TO INVEST IN?

Adoration

"THE SON RADIATES GOD'S OWN GLORY AND EXPRESSES THE VERY CHARACTER OF GOD, AND HE SUSTAINS EVERYTHING BY THE MIGHTY POWER OF HIS COMMAND. WHEN HE HAD CLEANSED US FROM OUR SINS, HE SAT DOWN IN THE PLACE OF HONOR AT THE RIGHT HAND OF THE MAJESTIC GOD IN HEAVEN."

- HEBREWS 1:3 (NLT)

_____

_____

_____

_____

_____

_____

_____

_____

_____

_____

_____

_____

Confession

"PEOPLE WHO CONCEAL THEIR SINS WILL NOT PROSPER,
BUT IF THEY CONFESS AND TURN FROM THEM, THEY WILL
RECEIVE MERCY."

- PROVERBS 28:13 (NLT)

_____

_____

_____

_____

_____

_____

_____

_____

_____

_____

_____

_____

_____

JESUS' OUTWARD-FOCUSED
COMMISSION, THE "GREAT
COMMISSION" NOT THE
"GREAT SUGGESTION," RE-
MAINS IN EFFECT FOR
EVERY CHRIST FOLLOWER
TO OBEY.

THANKSGIVING

"ALL OF THIS IS FOR YOUR BENEFIT. AND AS GOD'S GRACE REACHES MORE AND MORE PEOPLE, THERE WILL BE GREAT THANKSGIVING, AND GOD WILL RECEIVE MORE AND MORE GLORY."

- 2 CORINTHIANS 4:15 (NLT)

_____

_____

_____

_____

_____

_____

_____

_____

_____

_____

_____

_____

"SO LET US COME BOLDLY TO THE THRONE OF OUR GRACIOUS GOD. THERE WE WILL RECEIVE HIS MERCY, AND WE WILL FIND GRACE TO HELP US WHEN WE NEED IT MOST."

- HEBREWS 4:16 (NLT)

_____

_____

_____

_____

_____

_____

_____

_____

_____

_____

_____

_____

_____

WE ARE CHALLENGED TO PREACH THE GOOD NEWS OF HIS DEATH, BURIAL, AND RESURRECTION TO ALL NATIONS. THE SECOND CHALLENGE INSTRUCTS THEM TO WAIT IN JERUSALEM FOR THE PROMISED POWER, WHICH LUKE LATER DESCRIBES IN ACTS 1:8.

INTERCESSION

"ARE ANY OF YOU SICK? YOU SHOULD CALL FOR THE ELDERS OF THE CHURCH TO COME AND PRAY OVER YOU, ANOINTING YOU WITH OIL IN THE NAME OF THE LORD. SUCH A PRAYER OFFERED IN FAITH WILL HEAL THE SICK, AND THE LORD WILL MAKE YOU WELL. AND IF YOU HAVE COMMITTED ANY SINS, YOU WILL BE FORGIVEN."

- JAMES 5:14-15 (NLT)

PRAYER FOR FAMILY:
_____
_____

PRAYER FOR NEIGHBORS:
_____
_____

PRAYER FOR COMMUNITY:
_____
_____

PRAYER FOR COUNTRY:
_____
_____

PRAYER FOR WORLD:
_____
_____

Adoration

"THAT AT THE NAME OF JESUS EVERY KNEE SHOULD BOW,
IN HEAVEN AND ON EARTH AND UNDER THE EARTH"

- PHILIPPIANS 2:10 (NLT)

_____
_____
_____
_____
_____
_____
_____
_____
_____
_____
_____
_____

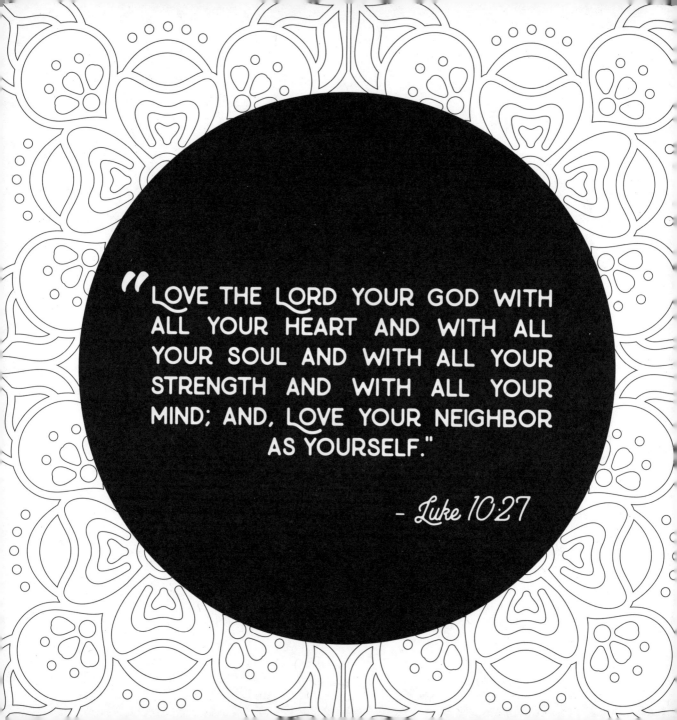

"LOVE THE LORD YOUR GOD WITH ALL YOUR HEART AND WITH ALL YOUR SOUL AND WITH ALL YOUR STRENGTH AND WITH ALL YOUR MIND; AND, LOVE YOUR NEIGHBOR AS YOURSELF."

- Luke 10:27

Confession

"IN THAT DAY UNGODLY FOOLS WILL NOT BE HEROES. SCOUNDRELS WILL NOT BE RESPECTED."

- ISAIAH 32:5 (NLT)

_____

_____

_____

_____

_____

_____

_____

_____

_____

_____

_____

_____

_____

_____

THANKSGIVING

"YES, YOU WILL BE ENRICHED IN EVERY WAY SO THAT YOU CAN ALWAYS BE GENEROUS. AND WHEN WE TAKE YOUR GIFTS TO THOSE WHO NEED THEM, THEY WILL THANK GOD."

- 2 CORINTHIANS 9:11 (NLT)

_____

_____

_____

_____

_____

_____

_____

_____

_____

_____

_____

_____

_____

THROUGH THE PARABLE OF THE GOOD SAMARITAN, JESUS ARTICULATED HOW PEOPLE SHOULD LOVE THEIR NEIGHBOR AS THEMSELVES. THIS OUTWARD FOCUSED DEMONSTRATION OF CARE AND CONCERN TURNED A SAMARITAN INTO A NEIGHBOR. JESUS CHALLENGES US TO DO THE SAME.

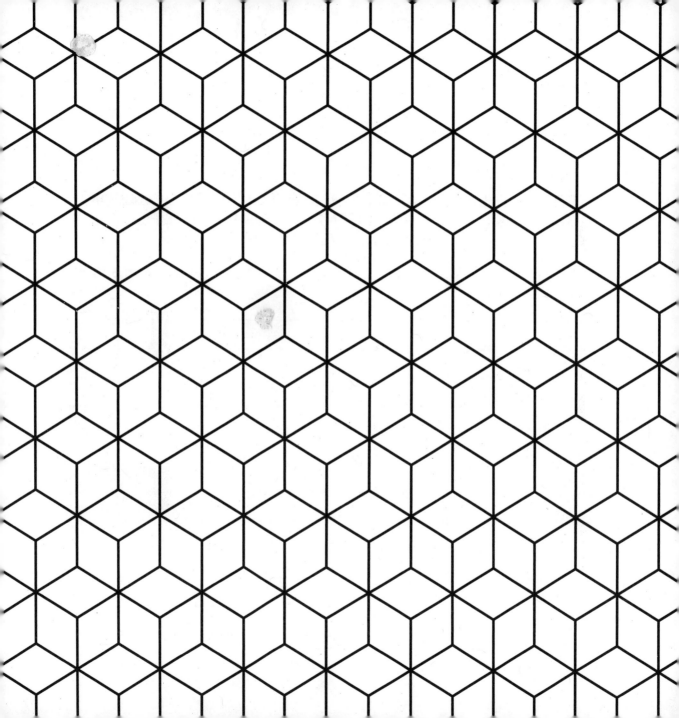

Supplication

"PRAY IN THE SPIRIT AT ALL TIMES AND ON EVERY OCCASION. STAY ALERT AND BE PERSISTENT IN YOUR PRAYERS FOR ALL BELIEVERS EVERYWHERE."

- EPHESIANS 6:18 (NLT)

_____

_____

_____

_____

_____

_____

_____

_____

_____

_____

_____

_____

_____

INTERCESSION

"BUT I SAY, LOVE YOUR ENEMIES!
PRAY FOR THOSE WHO PERSECUTE YOU!"

– MATTHEW 5:44 (NLT)

PRAYER FOR FAMILY:
_____

_____

PRAYER FOR NEIGHBORS:
_____

_____

PRAYER FOR COMMUNITY:
_____

_____

PRAYER FOR COUNTRY:
_____

_____

PRAYER FOR WORLD:
_____

_____

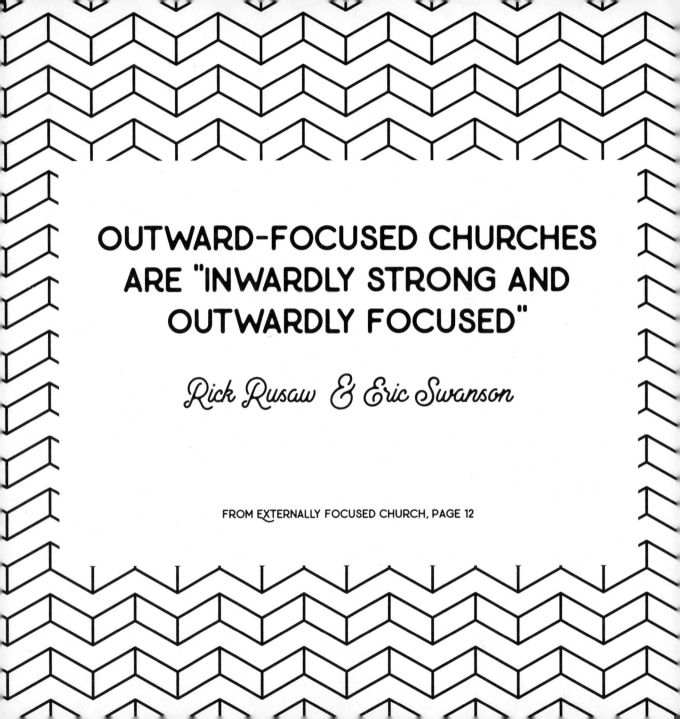

OUTWARD-FOCUSED CHURCHES ARE "INWARDLY STRONG AND OUTWARDLY FOCUSED"

Rick Rusaw & Eric Swanson

FROM EXTERNALLY FOCUSED CHURCH, PAGE 12

"AND THEN I HEARD EVERY CREATURE IN HEAVEN AND ON EARTH
AND UNDER THE EARTH AND IN THE SEA. THEY SANG:

'BLESSING AND HONOR AND GLORY AND POWER
BELONG TO THE ONE SITTING ON THE THRONE
AND TO THE LAMB FOREVER AND EVER.'"

– REVELATION 5:13 (NLT)

_____

_____

_____

_____

_____

_____

_____

_____

_____

_____

_____

_____

Confession

"NOW REPENT OF YOUR SINS AND TURN TO GOD,
SO THAT YOUR SINS MAY BE WIPED AWAY."

— ACTS 3:19 (NLT)

_____

_____

_____

_____

_____

_____

_____

_____

_____

_____

_____

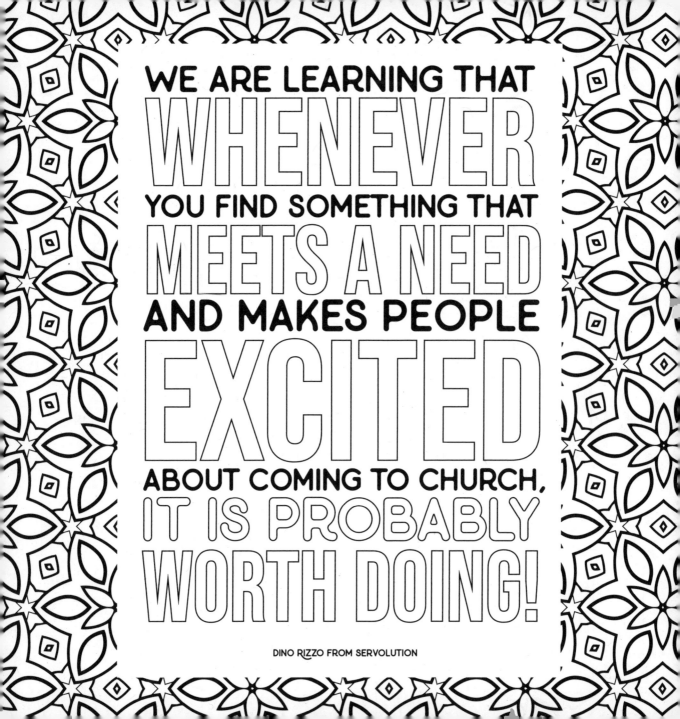

WE ARE LEARNING THAT WHENEVER YOU FIND SOMETHING THAT MEETS A NEED AND MAKES PEOPLE EXCITED ABOUT COMING TO CHURCH, IT IS PROBABLY WORTH DOING!

DINO RIZZO FROM SERVOLUTION

THANKSGIVING

"THERE WILL BE JOY AND SONGS OF THANKSGIVING,
AND I WILL MULTIPLY MY PEOPLE, NOT DIMINISH THEM;
I WILL HONOR THEM, NOT DESPISE THEM."

- JEREMIAH 30:19 (NLT)

_____

_____

_____

_____

_____

_____

_____

_____

_____

_____

_____

_____

Supplication

"THEY ALL MET TOGETHER AND WERE CONSTANTLY UNITED IN PRAYER, ALONG WITH MARY THE MOTHER OF JESUS, SEVERAL OTHER WOMEN, AND THE BROTHERS OF JESUS."

- ACTS 1:14 (NLT)

_____
_____
_____
_____
_____
_____
_____
_____
_____
_____
_____
_____
_____
_____

MISSIONS IS MORE THAN A PROGRAM OF THE CHURCH. MISSIONS IS WHO THE CHURCH IS BOTH AT HOME AND ABROAD.

INTERCESSION

"AND WORK FOR THE PEACE AND PROSPERITY OF THE CITY WHERE I SENT YOU INTO EXILE. PRAY TO THE LORD FOR IT, FOR ITS WELFARE WILL DETERMINE YOUR WELFARE."

– JEREMIAH 29:7 (NLT)

PRAYER FOR FAMILY: _____

_____

PRAYER FOR NEIGHBORS: _____

_____

PRAYER FOR COMMUNITY: _____

_____

PRAYER FOR COUNTRY: _____

_____

PRAYER FOR WORLD: _____

_____

Adoration

"FOR, THERE IS ONE GOD AND ONE MEDIATOR WHO CAN RECONCILE GOD AND HUMANITY—THE MAN CHRIST JESUS."

- 1 TIMOTHY 2:5 (NLT)

_____

_____

_____

_____

_____

_____

_____

_____

_____

_____

_____

_____

_____

"ORGANIZATIONS DON'T TAKE RISK, LEADERS TAKE RISK…THE LEADERS GOAL IS TO NARROW THE THINGS THE ORGANIZATION DOES TO JUST A FEW IMPORTANT THINGS…"

- Cheryl Bachelder
CEO OF POPEYES

Confession

"CONFESS YOUR SINS TO EACH OTHER AND PRAY FOR EACH OTHER SO THAT YOU MAY BE HEALED. THE EARNEST PRAYER OF A RIGHTEOUS PERSON HAS GREAT POWER AND PRODUCES WONDERFUL RESULTS."

– JAMES 5:16 (NLT)

_____

_____

_____

_____

_____

_____

_____

_____

_____

_____

_____

_____

_____

_____

THANKSGIVING

"I WILL PRAISE YOU, LORD, WITH ALL MY HEART;
I WILL TELL OF ALL THE MARVELOUS THINGS YOU HAVE DONE."

- PSALM 9:1 (NLT)

_____
_____
_____
_____
_____
_____
_____
_____
_____
_____
_____
_____
_____

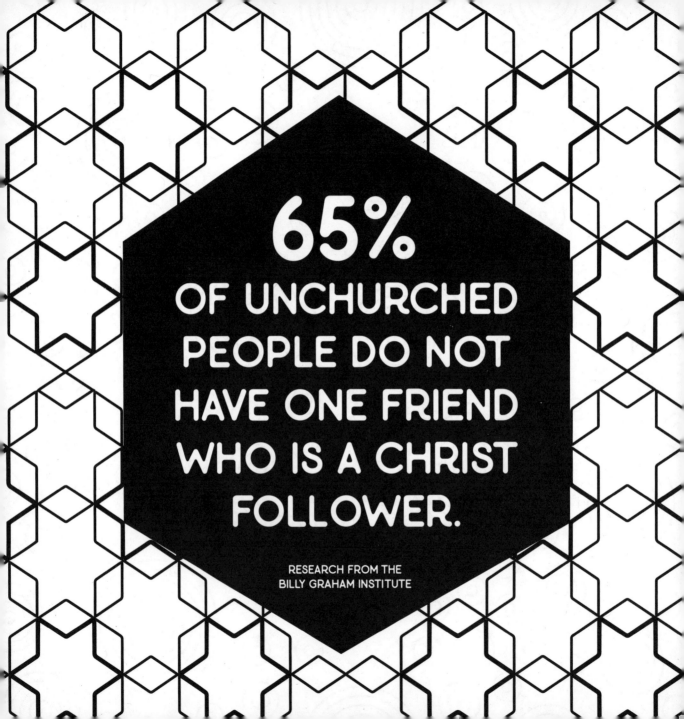

65%
OF UNCHURCHED
PEOPLE DO NOT
HAVE ONE FRIEND
WHO IS A CHRIST
FOLLOWER.

RESEARCH FROM THE
BILLY GRAHAM INSTITUTE

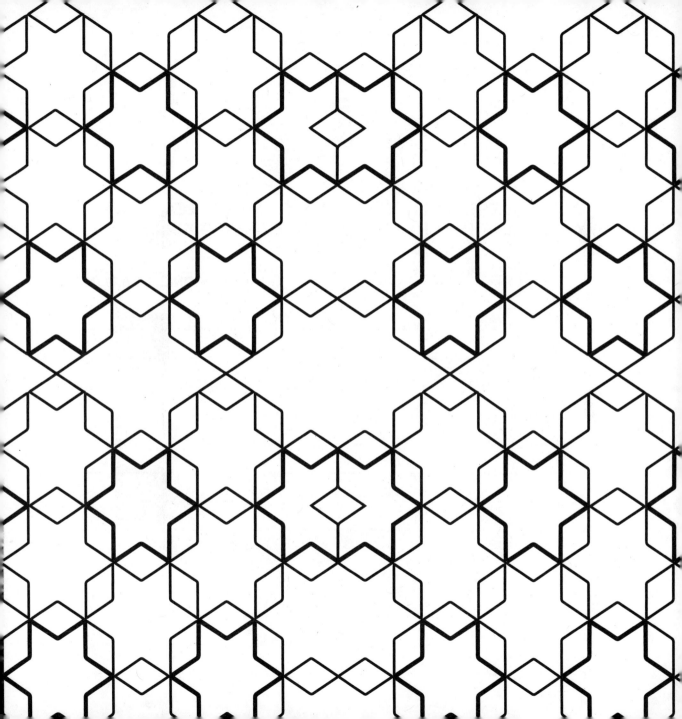

Supplication

"NEVERTHELESS, LISTEN TO MY PRAYER AND MY PLEA, O LORD MY GOD. HEAR THE CRY AND THE PRAYER THAT YOUR SERVANT IS MAKING TO YOU."

- 2 CHRONICLES 6:19 (NLT)

_____

_____

_____

_____

_____

_____

_____

_____

_____

_____

_____

_____

"FROM GENESIS TO REVELATION, THE READER IS PRESENTED WITH THE GOD OF MISSION. MISSION IS NOT A MARGINAL ACTIVITY OR DEPARTMENT OF THE CHURCH, BUT IT'S VERY HEARTBEAT. AS HAS OFTEN BEEN QUOTED, 'IT IS NOT THE CHURCH OF GOD THAT HAS A MISSION, BUT THE GOD OF MISSION WHO HAS A CHURCH.'"

- Eddie Gibbs

INTERCESSION

"BUT I HAVE PLEADED IN PRAYER FOR YOU, SIMON, THAT YOUR FAITH SHOULD NOT FAIL. SO WHEN YOU HAVE REPENTED AND TURNED TO ME AGAIN, STRENGTHEN YOUR BROTHERS."

- LUKE 22:32 (NLT)

PRAYER FOR FAMILY: _____

_____

PRAYER FOR NEIGHBORS: _____

_____

PRAYER FOR COMMUNITY: _____

_____

PRAYER FOR COUNTRY: _____

_____

PRAYER FOR WORLD: _____

_____

ADDITIONAL RESOURCES BY
DR. DAVE E. COLE

Additional resources available from the
Outward-Focused Network.

WHAT THE CHURCH CAN LEARN
FROM HARLEY DAVIDSON

REFOCUS: CREATING AN OUTWARD-FOCUSED
CHURCH CULTURE

REFOCUS - OUTWARD-FOCUSED
JOURNEY WORKBOOK

Learn more at www.outwardfocused.com

OUTWARD-FOCUSED CHURCH
SEMINARS:

Learn more at www.outwardfocused.com

ABOUT THE AUTHOR

DAVE E. COLE

Prior to becoming a pastor, while still attending college, Dave co-owned and operated a painting company in the Seattle area that grew overnight to become a successful business.

Following college, Dave pastored a growing church in East Wenatchee, Washington for 20 years with his wife Debbie. While in Wenatchee, Dave and other denominational leaders helped to meet the needs of hundreds of people every month by creating an outward-focused ministry, *Serve Wenatchee Valley*.

He was elected as Assistant Superintendent for the Northwest Ministry Network of the Assemblies of God in 2002, and he continues to work with hundreds of pastors and congregations who desire to move beyond the status quo of church ministry. Dave recently focused his doctoral studies in developing an outward-focused church culture. He serves as Adjunct Professor for Northwest University in Kirkland, Washington.

His experience in both secular business and the Church world brings a broad base of knowledge and expertise. Dave is able to use this to help organizations and churches shift from an inward-focused to an outward-focused culture.

JON WREN

Feeling a call to ministry from an early age, Jon pursued ministry whole-heartedly. Jon received his B.A. in Philosophy & Religion and Liberal Arts with an emphasis in Pastoral Ministry and his M.A. in Missional Leadership from Northwest Nazarene University located in Nampa, Idaho. He has been on a journey to understand what ministry looks like centered around mission.

Seeing a need for design and web-development specifically in church contexts, Jon and his father, Carl, founded Wren Designed LLP. Wren Designed LLP seeks to provide affordable, effective aesthetic solutions for churches and non-profits. Coupled with Jon & Carl's ministry, Wren Designed LLP has opened ministry doors for a multitude of churches and non-profits across the nation.

Jon has pastored Life Community Church in Snoqualmie, Washington since 2016. Working with other local pastors, Jon sees a vision of God on mission and at work in Snoqualmie, in Washington, and beyond.

Jon's expertise lies not only in effective design solutions but in creating a missional ministry. Working with Dave Cole since 2017, Jon and Dave hope to see their ministries work to benefit pastors, leaders, and the world.